Christian Crafts for Christmas Paper Plates

by

Rebecca Daniel

and

Janet Skiles

illustrated by Janet Skiles

Cover by Janet Skiles

Copyright © 1993

Shining Star Publications

ISBN No. 0-86653-756-2

Standardized Subject Code TA ac

Printing No. 98765432

Shining Star Publications
1204 Buchanan St., Box 299
Carthage, IL 62321-0299

Unless otherwise indicated, the New International Version of the Bible was used in preparing the activities in this book.

Table of Contents

To the Teacher/Parent

This book has been created to educate as well as entertain young children. The basic focus is for younger children, but older youngsters will also enjoy making and using the paper plate projects especially designed to celebrate Christmas and winter.

Paper plate crafts are ideal for use in Sunday School. They are sturdy and easily adapted to a wide variety of projects. This book is designed to give a sampling of many different crafts that can be created using paper plates. All the materials used in these projects are easily obtained. The thin, inexpensive paper plates will make the best basic forms. Do not use plastic or Styrofoam™ plates because they are usually too thick for most projects. The step-by-step directions and patterns for each project make this book easy to use and guarantee built-in success. As you work on these crafts, encourage the children to use their own ideas and imaginations. The goal is not perfection, but learning more about the Christmas story and other Bible-based stories.

Although patterns are given, it is important to stress to the children that there is not one right way to make each project. Projects vary and ultimately should make children feel good about themselves and their unique art styles. Encourage older children to create their own patterns instead of using those found in the book. Directions are provided, but children should be allowed to make each project in their own fashions. Give them as much freedom as possible in choosing color combinations and design placement. In children's art it is the process, not the product, that is most important.

Dedication

For Janet, Nancee, Vanessa, Dan, Judy, Tom, and
all the other wonderful artists at Shining Star.
Thank you for making my books shine!
Becky

To Bo, my most trusted friend,
Janet

"Rejoice" Bell

"Rejoice in the Lord, you who are righteous, and praise his holy name."

Psalm 97:12

Materials:
    One 9" paper plate
    Paints, crayons, colored pencils, or
      markers
    Scissors
    Yarn
    Three small jingle bells
    Construction paper (optional)
    Glue
    Glitter (optional)
    Hole punch

Related Scripture:
    Psalm 33:1
    Isaiah 61:10

Directions:

1. Reproduce and cut out the bell pattern on page 6. Trace the bell pattern on the paper plate, color, and cut out.

2. Reproduce, color, and cut out the lettering. Glue to the bell. Punch three holes in the lettering pattern as indicated (Figure 1).

3. Reproduce, color, and cut out the bell clanger, and glue to the back of the bell. Decorate the bell with construction paper cutouts or glitter as desired (Figure 2).

4. Tie different lengths of yarn to the jingle bells. To attach jingle bells to the bell, thread yarn through the holes in the lettering pattern and tie. To make a hanger for the bell, punch another hole in the top of the bell. Thread yarn through the hole and tie (Figure 3).

Figure 1   Figure 2   Figure 3

SS2871

6

SS2871

Silent Night in Bethlehem

"But you, Bethlehem . . . out of you will come a ruler who will be the shepherd of my people Israel."   Matthew 2:6

Materials:
   One 9" paper plate
   Paints, crayons, colored pencils, or
      markers
   Blue construction paper
   Foil stars (optional)
   Sand or sandpaper
   Scissors
   Glue

Related Scripture:
   Matthew 2:1-5
   Luke 2:4

Directions:
   1. Draw a 6" circle in the center of the paper plate. Cut out the circle. Color the front of the remaining paper plate blue (Figure 1).

   2. Cut a 7" circle out of blue construction paper. Reproduce, color, and cut out the Bethlehem pattern on page 8. Glue to the construction paper circle. Glue sand or sandpaper to the bottom of the Bethlehem picture (Figure 2).

   3. Glue the Bethlehem picture to the back of the paper plate so that it shows through the hole in the paper plate.

   4. Reproduce, color, and cut out the lettering and the star. Glue to the plate rim (Figure 3).

Figure 1

Figure 2

Figure 3

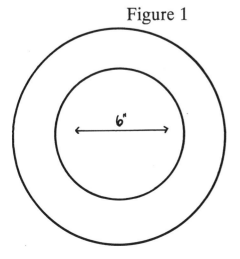

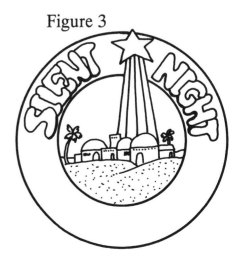

SS2871

SILENT NIGHT

SS2871

"Glory to God" Candle

"You, O Lord, keep my lamp burning; my God turns my darkness into light."   Psalm 18:28

Materials:
   One 9" paper plate
   Paints, crayons, colored pencils, or
      markers
   Scissors
   Glue
   Gold or white glitter
   Light cardboard or heavy stock

Related Scripture:
   Luke 11:36
   Proverbs 20:27

Directions:

1. Color the back of the paper plate light yellow.

2. On light cardboard or heavy stock, reproduce, color, and cut out the candle pattern on page 10. Glue to the back of the paper plate as shown (Figure 1).

3. Color the circle of light around the flame dark yellow. Spread the light-beam area with glue. Sprinkle with gold or white glitter. When dry, shake off excess glitter (Figure 2).

4. Color the flame of the candle dark yellow or orange.

5. Reproduce, color, and cut out the lettering. Glue to the rim of the plate (Figure 3).

Figure 1   Figure 2    Figure 3

Patterns

SS2871

"Peace Dove" Ornament

"Glory to God in the highest, and on earth peace to men on whom his favor rests."   Luke 2:14

Materials:
    One 9" paper plate
    Paints, crayons, colored pencils, or
        markers
    Black fine-tip marker
    Scissors
    Hole punch
    Yarn
    Glue
    Tape

Related Scripture:
    John 14:27
    Isaiah 26:3

Directions:
1. Reproduce and cut out the bird and wing patterns on page 12. Trace them onto the paper plate and cut out. Use a black fine-tip marker to draw details on the bird as indicated on the pattern (Figure 1).
2. Cut a slit on the body where indicated, and insert wings through the slit. Secure wings with a small piece of tape under each wing (Figure 2).
3. Reproduce, color, and cut out the lettering, and glue one to each side of the body of the bird.
4. Punch a hole in the body where indicated. To create a hanger for the bird, thread yarn through the hole and tie (Figure 3).

Figure 1   Figure 2   Figure 3

SS2871

Patterns

Fold

PEACE

SS2871

Nativity Mobile

"For to us a child is born, to us a son is given, and the government will be on his shoulders."

Isaiah 9:6a

Materials:
 One 9" paper plate
 Crayons, colored pencils, or markers
 Yarn
 One pipe cleaner
 Tape
 Glue
 Scissors

Related Scripture:
 Luke 2:4-12
 Isaiah 7:14

 Hole punch
 Glitter
 Light cardboard or heavy
  stock

Directions:
1. Cut off 1 ¾" from the paper plate as shown (Figure 1). Color the front of the plate dark blue.
2. Reproduce, color, and cut out the manger on page 14 and glue to the plate.
3. Punch holes in the plate where indicated.
4. On light cardboard or heavy stock, reproduce, color, and cut out the mobile patterns on pages 15 and 16. Punch a hole in each one where indicated. Attach the mobile patterns to the manger scene using a variety of yarn lengths (Figure 2).
5. Reproduce, color, and cut out the star on page 16. Decorate with glitter. Glue to the top of the manger.
6. Reproduce, color, and cut out the angel on page 16. For a three-dimensional look, bend and tape the pipe cleaner to the back of the angel, and insert the other end of the pipe cleaner through a hole punched in the paper plate rim. Bend and secure the pipe cleaner to the back of the plate rim with tape (Figure 3).

Figure 1

Figure 2

Figure 3

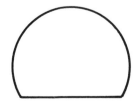

SS2871

Pattern

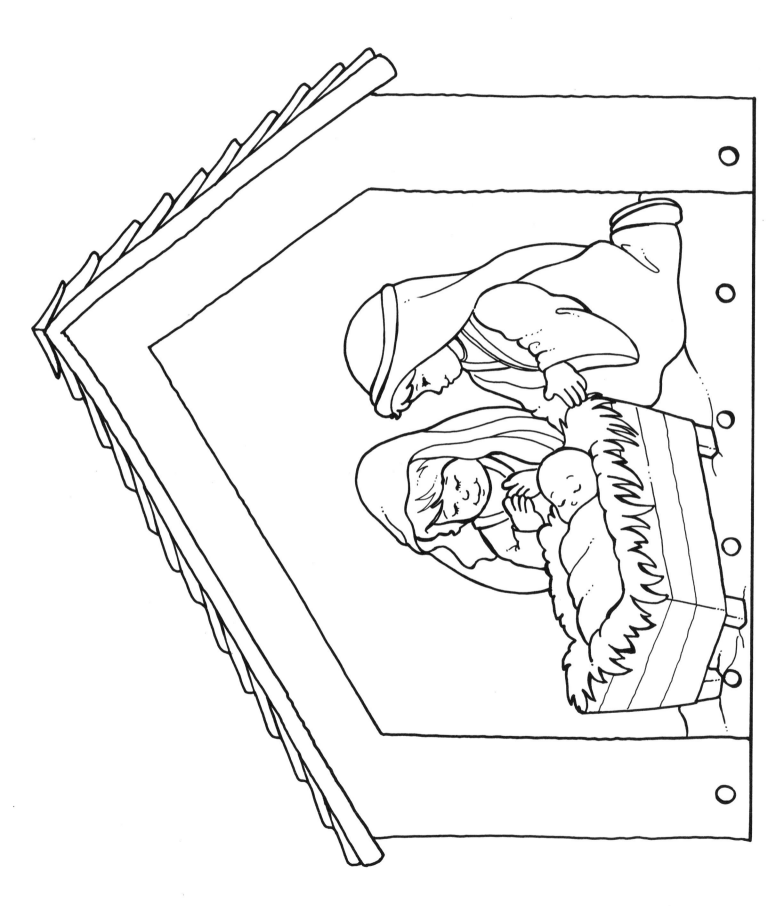

SS2871

Patterns

SS2871

Patterns

Shining Star Publications. Copyright © 1993

SS2871

Angel Centerpiece

"Suddenly a great company of the heavenly host appeared with the angel, praising God and saying, 'Glory to God in the highest, and on earth peace to men on whom his favor rests.' "   Luke 2:13-14

Materials: Related Scripture:
   One 9" paper plate   Luke 1:26-33
   Paints, crayons, colored pencils, or   Luke 2:8-12
     markers
   Glue
   Scissors
   Stapler
   Sequins, rickrack, or glitter
   Cotton balls

Directions:
1. Cut the paper plate in half, and color one of the halves. Roll into a cone shape, overlap, and glue or staple where needed to secure (Figure 1).

2. Reproduce, color, and cut out the angel pattern on page 18. Fold on the dotted line and glue to the cone (Figure 2).

3. Decorate the angel with sequins, rickrack, or glitter.

4. For a cloud effect, glue cotton balls to the rim of the paper plate (Figure 3).

Figure 1   Figure 2   Figure 3

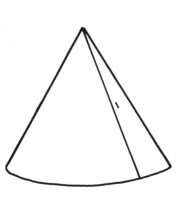  

Pattern

Fold

SS2871

"Joy to the World" Ornament

"The angel said . . . 'I bring you good news of great joy that will be for all the people.' "   Luke 2:10

Materials: Related Scripture:
    Two 9" paper plates   Luke 15:7
    Paints, crayons, colored pencils, or   John 15:9-11
      markers
    Scissors
    Hole punch
    Yarn or ribbon
    Glue

Directions:

1. Paint or color the back of each paper plate.

2. Reproduce, color, and cut out the ornament top on page 20, and glue it to the front rim of one of the paper plates (Figure 1). Reverse the pattern, and repeat the procedure using the other paper plate.

3. Put glue on the edge of the front side of both paper plates, and place them together. Add glue to the inside edges of the ornament tops, and press them together. Let them dry (Figure 2).

4. Reproduce, color, and cut out the lettering, and glue one to each side of the ornament.

5. Punch a hole in the ornament top. To make a hanger, string a piece of yarn or ribbon through the hole, and tie (Figure 3).

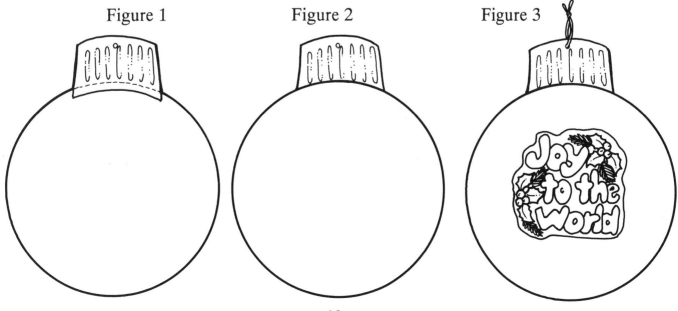

Figure 1   Figure 2   Figure 3

SS2871

Patterns

Apply glue here.

SS2871

Giant Snowman

"He spreads the snow like wool and scatters the frost like ashes."

Psalm 147:16

Materials:
Two 9" paper plates
One 6" paper plate
Paints, crayons, colored pencils, or
    markers
Scissors
Glue
Cotton batting or cotton balls
Yarn
Stapler (optional)

Related Scripture:
Psalm 51:7
Isaiah 55:10-11

Directions:

1. Overlap paper plate backs about an inch. Trim the area where the plates meet so they fit together smoothly. Glue or staple the plates together (Figure 1).

2. Glue cotton batting or flattened cotton balls to the surface of the paper plates.

3. Reproduce, color, and cut out the hat, arm, glove, and face features on pages 22 and 23. Glue onto the plates as shown (Figure 2).

4. Reproduce, color, and cut out the scarf. Glue 1" yarn pieces to the back of the end of the scarf. Glue the scarf to the snowman.

5. Reproduce, color, and cut out the gift box. Glue the gift box inside the arms so that the snowman is holding the gifts (Figure 3).

Figure 1

Figure 2

Figure 3

SS2871

Patterns

SS2871

Patterns

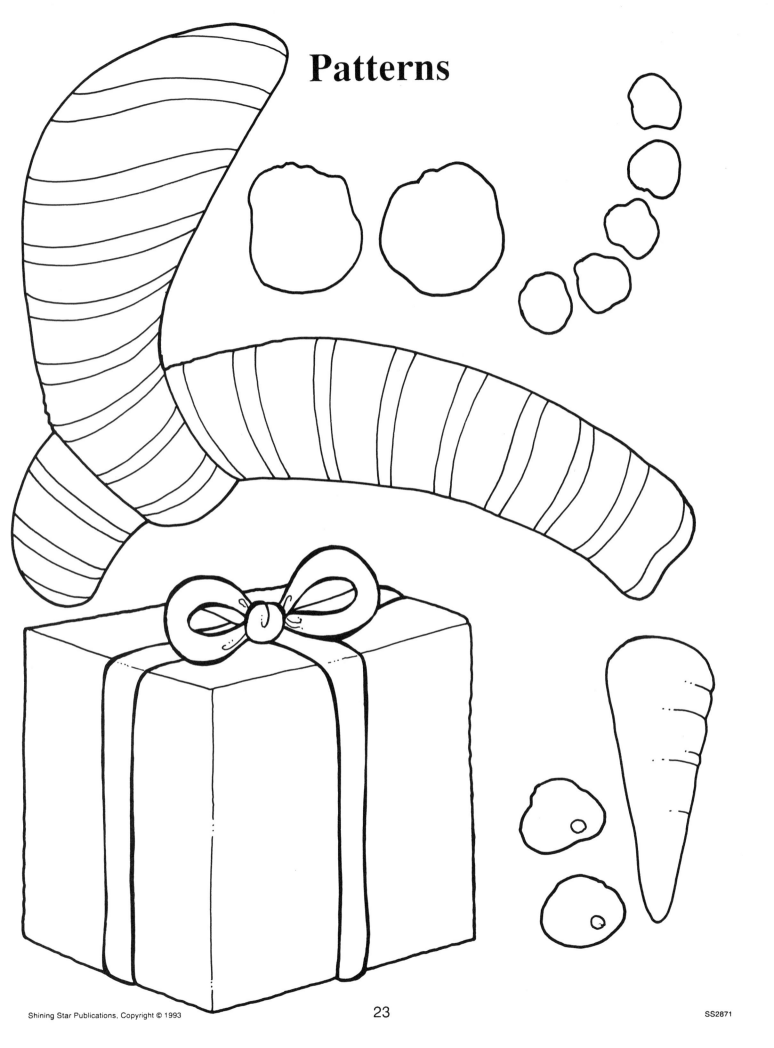

SS2871

Lovable Lamb

"I am the good shepherd; I know my sheep and my sheep know me . . . ."

John 10:14

Materials:
  One 9" paper plate
  Paints, crayons, colored pencils, or
    markers
  Scissors
  Glue
  Cotton balls

Related Scripture:
  Proverbs 27:25-26
  Isaiah 40:11

Directions:
  1. Reproduce, color, and cut out the lamb's head, legs, and tail on pages 25 and 26. Glue to the front of the paper plate. Make sure the ear overlaps the plate as shown (Figure 1).

  2. Glue cotton balls to the body and head (Figure 2).

  3. Reproduce, color, and cut out the holly, and glue it to the neck of the lamb (Figure 3).

Figure 1   Figure 2   Figure 3

SS2871

Patterns

SS2871

Patterns

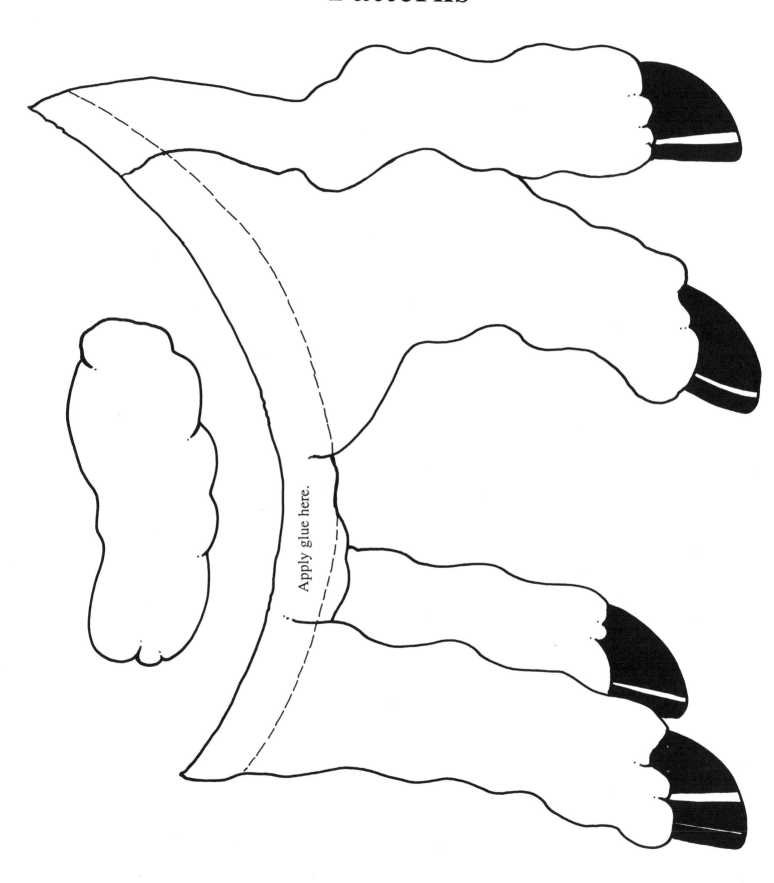

Apply glue here.

SS2871

Family Wreath

"But He lifted the needy out of their affliction and increased their families like flocks."   Psalm 107:41

Materials:
  Two 9" paper plates
  Crayons, colored pencils, or
    markers
  Yarn
  Scissors
  Glue
  Hole punch

Related Scripture:
  Leviticus 25:10
  Joshua 24:15

Directions:

1. Draw a circle with a 6" diameter in the center of one paper plate, and cut it out. Color the back of the plate green.

2. Reproduce, color, and cut out the holly pattern on page 28. You will need at least seven copies so that the rim is covered. Overlapping slightly, glue them to the plate (Figure 1).

3. Reproduce, color, and cut out the bow. Glue to the plate.

4. Draw and color a picture of your family or another scene on the front center of the other paper plate (Figure 2).

5. Glue the two plates together with the front rims facing each other (Figure 3).

6. Punch a hole at the center near the top, and insert yarn. Tie the ends together, and use it to hang the wreath.

Figure 1

Figure 2

Figure 3

Patterns

SS2871

Dove Greeting Card or Invitation

"As soon as Jesus was baptized, he went up out of the water. At that moment heaven was opened, and he saw the Spirit of God descending like a dove and lighting on him."   Matthew 3:16

Materials:
    One 9" paper plate
    Crayons, paints, colored pencils, or
      markers
    Scissors
    Glue

Related Scripture:
    Genesis 8:8-12
    Psalm 55:6

Directions:
1. Reproduce and cut out the dove pattern on page 30. Trace it onto the paper plate, and cut it out (Figure 1).
2. Reproduce, color, and cut out the holly pattern. Cut a slit in the bird's beak, and insert the holly (Figure 2).
3. Fold over the wing on the dotted line, and write a greeting or message on the body (Figure 3).

Figure 1   Figure 2   Figure 3

Patterns

Fold

SS2871

Jingle Bells Christmas Stocking

"Yet I will rejoice in the Lord, I will be joyful in God my Savior."

Habakkuk 3:18

Materials:
- Two 9" paper plates
- Paints, crayons, colored pencils, or markers
- Three jingle bells
- Green or red yarn
- Scissors
- Glue
- Hole Punch

Related Scripture:
- Ezra 6:22
- Acts 8:4-8

Directions:

1. Reproduce and cut out the stocking pattern on page 32. Trace it onto a plate, and cut it out. Repeat, using the other paper plate. Leaving the top edge open, glue the edges of the two stockings together (Figure 1).

2. When glue is thoroughly dry, punch holes evenly around the edges of the stocking except across the top. Beginning at the top, lace or "sew" the yarn through the holes, and tie at each end.

3. Using three of the holes that you used to lace the two stockings together, attach the jingle bells to the stocking with yarn (Figure 2).

4. To create a hanger for the stocking, punch a hole at the top of one side of the stocking, thread yarn through the hole, and tie.

5. Reproduce, color, and cut out the stocking decorations. Glue them to the stocking (Figure 3).

Figure 1   Figure 2   Figure 3

SS2871

Patterns

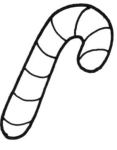

32

Sweet Candy Cane

"Pleasant words are a honeycomb, sweet to the soul and healing to the bones."   Proverbs 16:24

Materials:
    One 9" paper plate
    Paints, crayons, colored pencils, or
        markers
    Scissors
    Hole punch
    Glue
    Yarn or ribbon

Related Scripture:
    Psalm 145:15-16
    James 1:17

Directions:
1. Reproduce and cut out the cane pattern on page 34. Trace it onto the paper plate. Color it, and cut it out (Figure 1).

2. Reproduce, color, and cut out the holly and berries. Glue to the candy cane (Figure 2).

3. Reproduce, color, and cut out the gift tag. Punch a hole in the candy cane and a hole in the gift tag. Use yarn or ribbon to attach the gift tag to the candy cane (Figure 3).

Figure 1   Figure 2   Figure 3

SS2871

Patterns

SS2871

Christmas Crowns

"Mordecai left the king's presence wearing royal garments of blue and white, a large crown of gold and a purple robe of fine linen. . . ." Esther 8:15

Materials:
 Two 9" paper plates
 Crayons, colored pencils, or markers
 Glitter, sequins, ribbon, etc.
 Tape
 Glue
 Scissors

Related Scripture:
 Psalm 21:3
 Zechariah 9:16

 Stapler (optional)
 Tagboard or lightweight cardboard
 Cotton balls (for angel pattern)

Directions:

1. Trace, color, and cut out the desired hat pattern on page 36 eight times–four on each paper plate (Figure 1).

2. Decorate with glitter, sequins, ribbon, etc.

3. Cut a 1½" x 11" piece of tagboard for a headband. With the front side of the patterns toward the inside of the headband, glue or tape patterns spaced evenly around the headband (Figure 2).

4. Tape or staple another cardboard strip to the band and adjust to the size of the head (Figure 3).

5. Add cotton balls to the headbands of angel crowns to represent clouds.

Figure 1   Figure 2   Figure 3

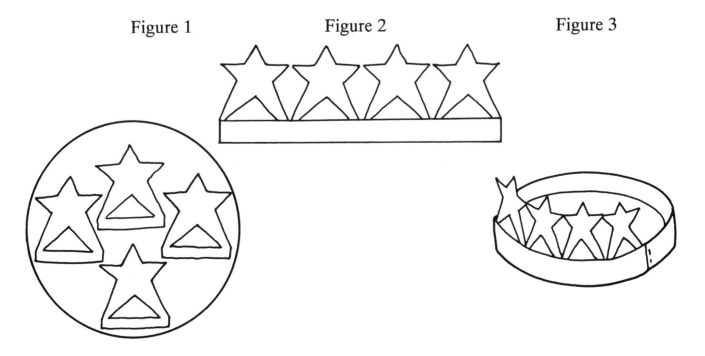

SS2871

Patterns

Apply glue here.

Apply glue here.

Apply glue here.

Apply glue here.

SS2871

Shepherd Greeting Card Holder

"And there were shepherds living out in the fields nearby, keeping watch over their flocks at night."   Luke 2:8

Materials: Related Scripture:
    Two 9" paper plates   Luke 2:15-20
    Paints, crayons, colored pencils, or   John 10:14
      markers
    Yarn
    Scissors
    Hole punch
    Glue

Directions:
1. Color the front of one paper plate dark blue.

2. Cut the second paper plate in half. Glue the front of one of the halves to the front of the dark blue plate to form a pocket. Apply glue only to the rim of the plate half and the corresponding rim of the dark blue plate (Figure 1).

3. Punch holes evenly around the glued rims of the plates. Beginning on either side, lace or "sew" the yarn through the holes and tie at each end (Figure 2).

4. Reproduce, color, and cut out the holly, shepherd and sheep, and star patterns on page 38. Glue to the paper plates as shown (Figure 3).

Figure 1   Figure 2   Figure 3

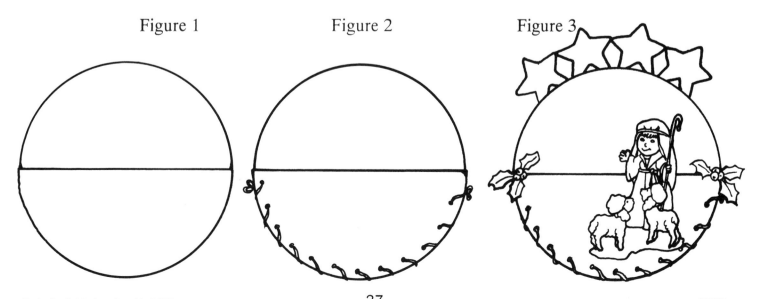

                                                                          SS2871

Patterns

Apply glue here.

Gingerbread Kids

"Jesus said, 'Let the little children come to me, and do not hinder them, for the kingdom of heaven belongs to such as these.' "   Matthew 19:14

Materials:
    Two 9" paper plates
    Paints, crayons, colored pencils, or
        markers
    Glitter, rickrack, cloth scraps
    Construction paper
    Scissors
    Glue

Related Scripture:
    Matthew 18:3
    Ephesians 5:8

Directions:
1. Color the backs of both plates brown.
2. Reproduce, color, and cut out the patterns on pages 40-43 from construction paper. Glue the vest on one plate and the dress on the other (Figure 1).
3. Color the arms and legs the same color as the paper plate backs, and glue them into place as shown (Figure 2).
4. Glue on the face, bow, and icing decorations. Decorate each gingerbread kid with glitter, rickrack, cloth cutouts, etc. (Figure 3).

Figure 1   Figure 2    Figure 3

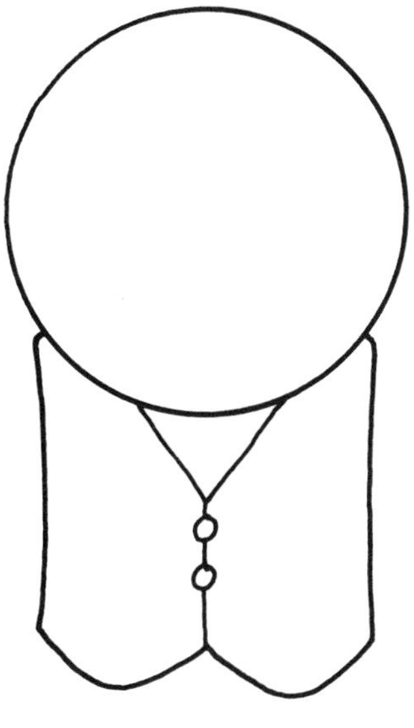

          SS2871

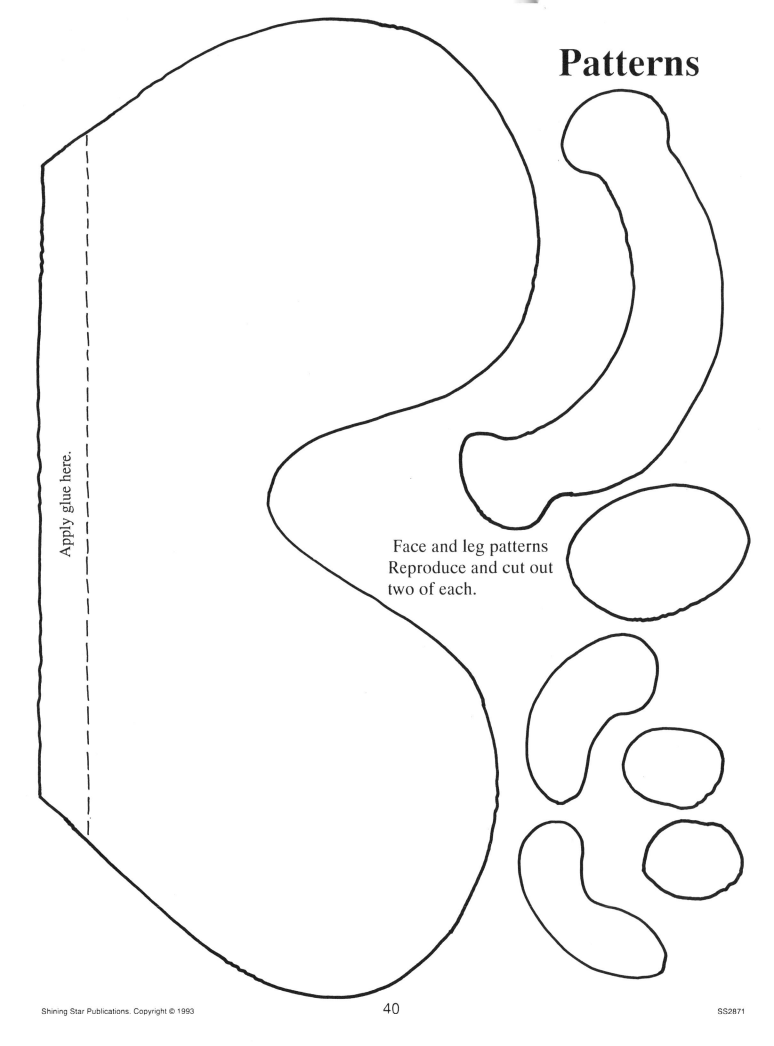

Patterns

Apply glue here.

Face and leg patterns
Reproduce and cut out
two of each.

SS2871

Patterns

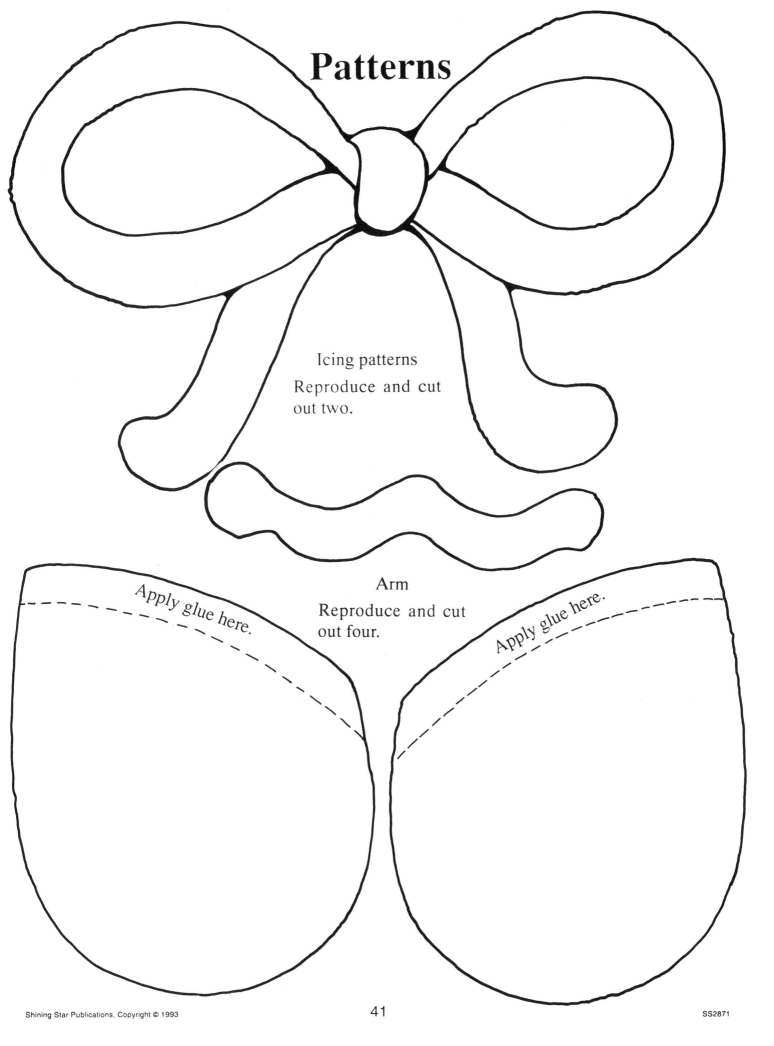

Icing patterns
Reproduce and cut
out two.

Arm
Reproduce and cut
out four.

Apply glue here.

Apply glue here.

41

SS2871

Patterns

Boy's vest

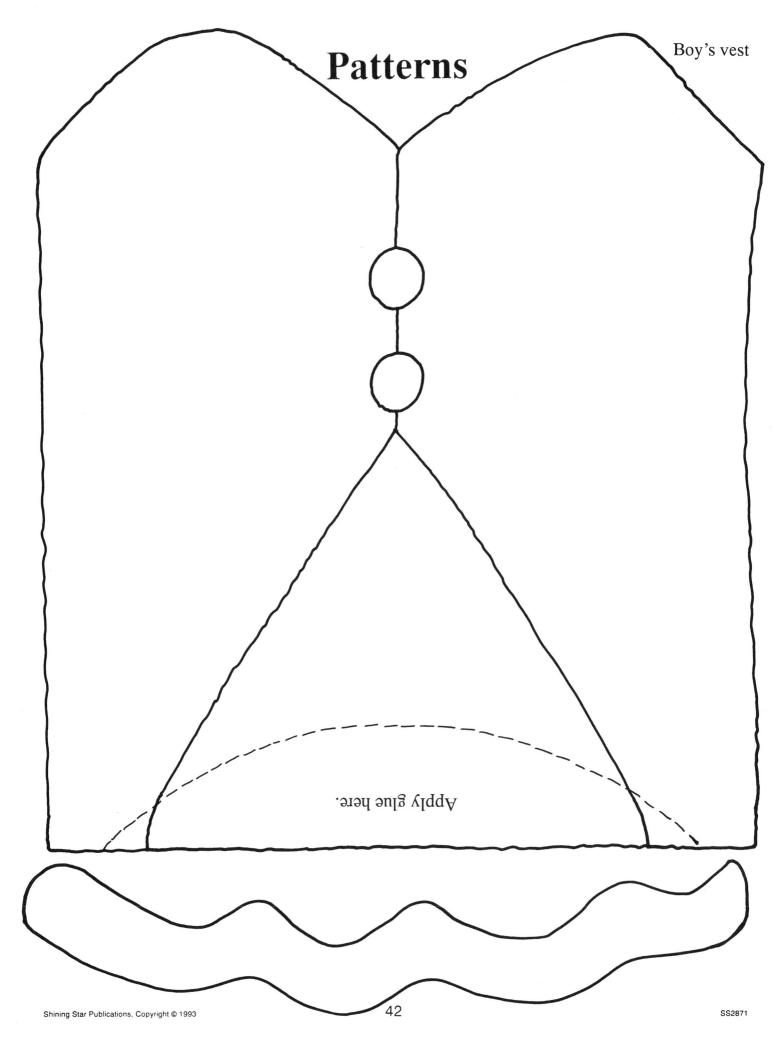

Apply glue here.

SS2871

Pattern

Girl's dress

Apply glue here.

SS2871

"Joy" Door Decoration

"And all the people went up after him, playing flutes and rejoicing greatly. . . ."

1 Kings 1:40

Materials:
- One 9" paper plate
- Paints, crayons, colored pencils, or markers
- Scissors
- Tagboard
- Glue
- Gift wrapping paper, glitter, rickrack, etc.

Related Scripture:
- Psalm 81:1
- Ezra 6:22

Directions:

1. Draw a circle with a 6" diameter in the center of the paper plate. Cut it out (Figure 1). Color the back of the plate green.

2. Reproduce, color, and cut out the bear and bow patterns on pages 45 and 46. Attach the bear and the bow to the paper plate as shown (Figure 2).

3. On tagboard, reproduce the J and Y patterns on pages 47 and 48. Color and cut out. Decorate the letters with glitter, gift wrapping paper, cutouts, rickrack, etc. Assemble the three pieces to spell JOY.

Figure 1   Figure 2

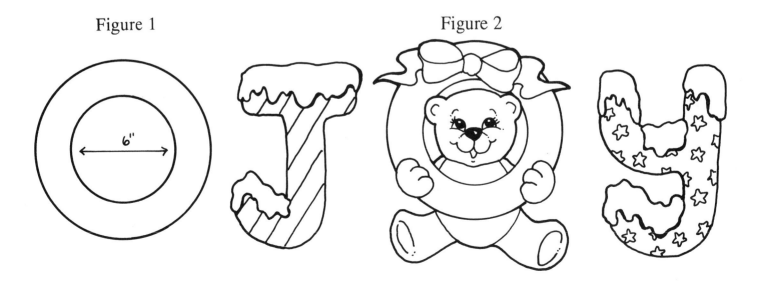

Patterns

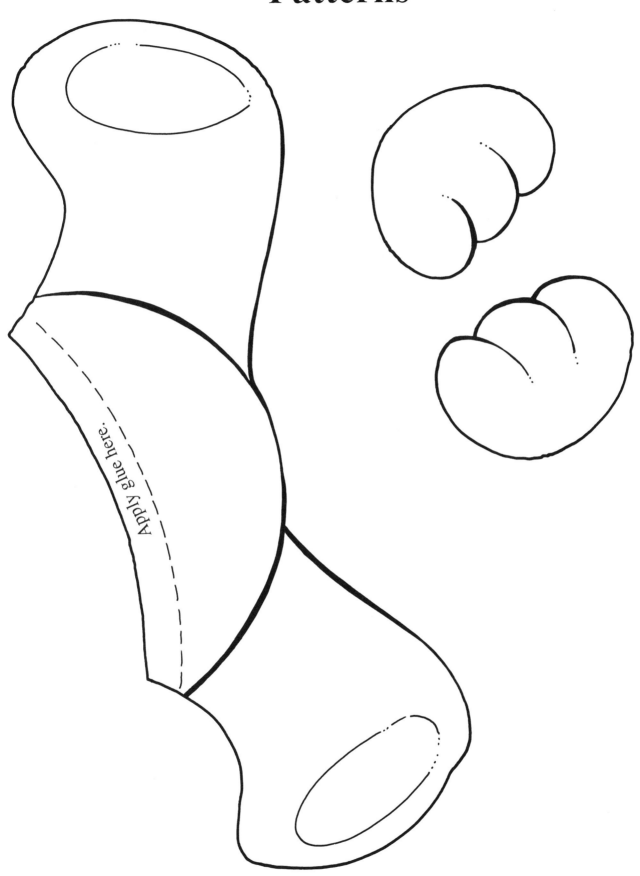

Apply glue here.

SS2871

Patterns

Apply glue here.

SS2871

Pattern

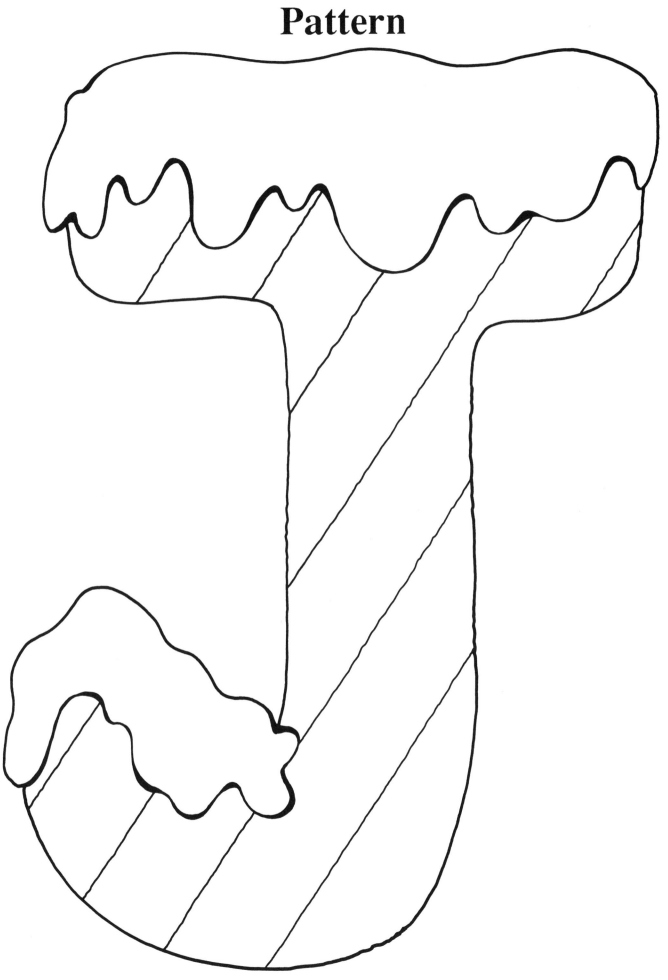

47

SS2871

Pattern

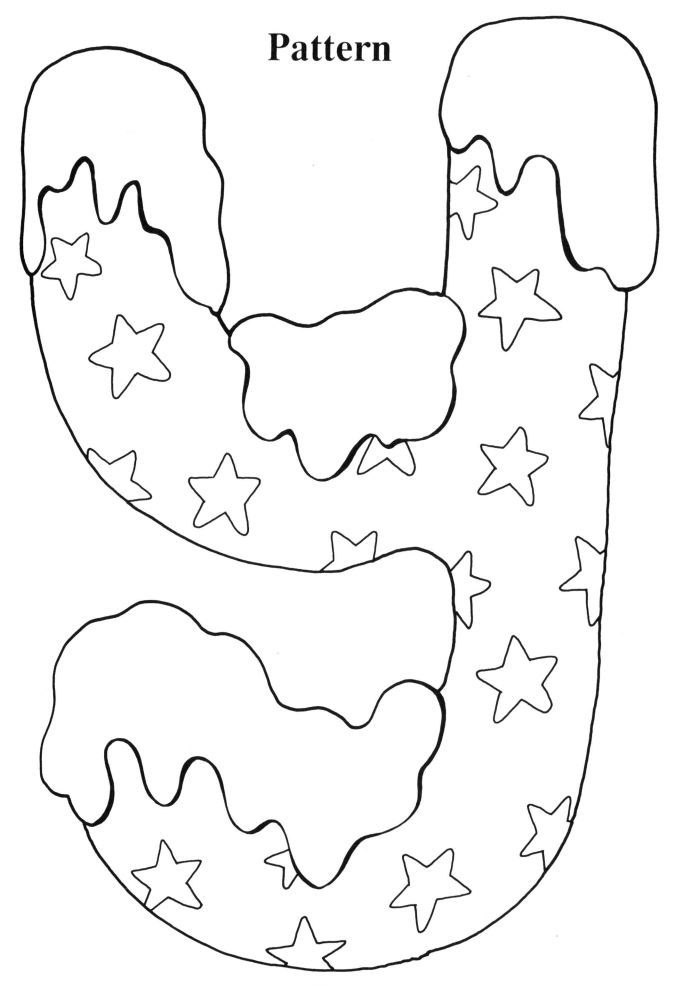

SS2871

Flying Angel

"In the sixth month, God sent the angel Gabriel to . . . Mary. The angel . . . said, 'Greetings, you who are highly favored! The Lord is with you.' "

Luke 1:26-28

Materials:
   One 6" paper plate
   Crayons, colored pencils or
      markers
   Yarn
   Glue
   Scissors
   Hole punch
   Glitter, felt scraps, Christmas
      garland, etc.

Related Scripture:
   Psalm 148:2
   Matthew 4:11

Directions:

1. Color the paper plate front using a skin tone color.

2. Reproduce, color, and cut out the hair and face on page 50. You may use felt for the hair. Attach with glue as shown (Figure 1).

3. Reproduce, color, and cut out the angel body, and glue to the 6" paper plate. If desired, decorate the angel's robe with felt pieces, glitter, or Christmas garland (Figure 2).

4. To make a hanger, punch a hole in the angel body, thread yarn through the hole, and tie (Figure 3).

Figure 1	Figure 2	Figure 3

SS2871

Patterns

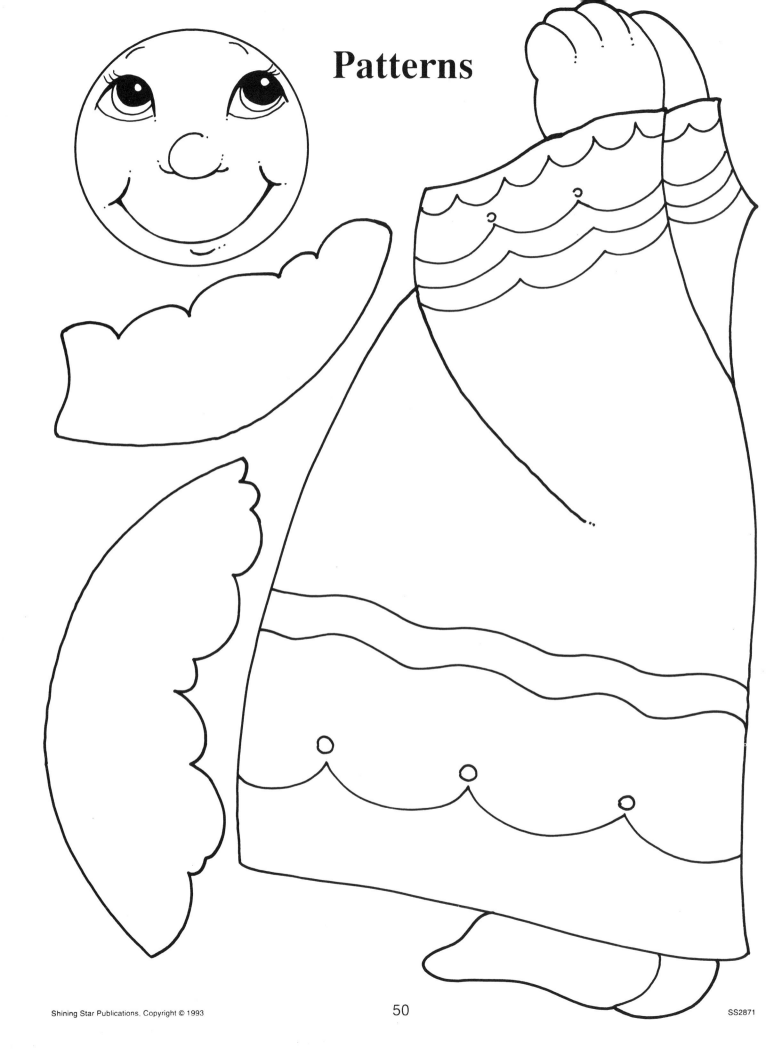

SS2871

Snowflakes

"He spreads the snow like wool and scatters the frost like ashes."

Psalm 147:16

Materials:
    One 9" or 6" paper plate
    Scissors
    Glue
    Glitter
    Hole punch
    Yarn

Related Scripture:
    Isaiah 55:10-11
    Job 37:5-6

Directions:

1. Fold the paper plate in half. Fold again in thirds (Figure 1).

2. Cut on the folds any shape desired (Figure 2). Open and admire. Each snowflake will be unique.

3. Spread glue on the snowflake. Decorate with glitter (Figure 3).

4. Punch a hole near the edge. Insert yarn, tie in a loop, and use for hanging the snowflake.

Figure 1   Figure 2 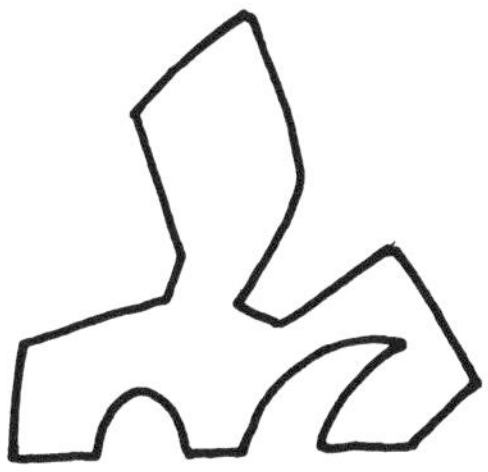   Figure 3

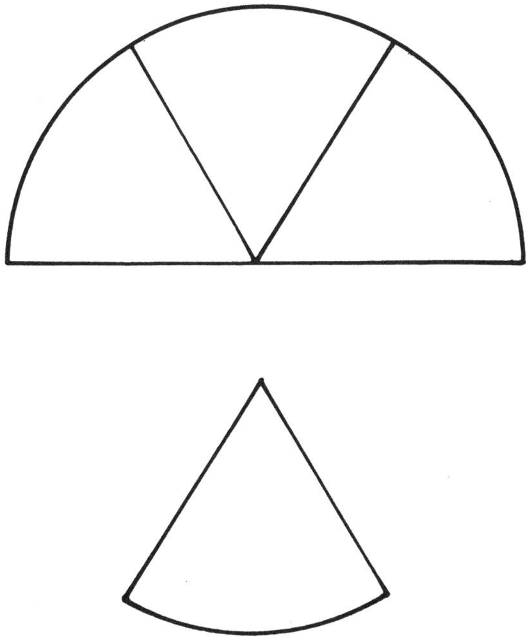

Shining Star Publications, Copyright © 1993   SS2871

Wintertime Bird Feeder

"Jesus replied, 'Foxes have holes and birds of the air have nests, but the Son of Man has no place to lay his head.' "   Matthew 8:20

Materials:
  One 9" paper plate
  Paints, crayons, colored pencils, or
    markers
  Stapler (optional)
  Hole punch
  Ribbon
  Scissors
  Glue

Related Scripture:
  Psalm 11:1
  Psalm 104:12

Directions:

1. Cut the paper plate in half and color one of the halves. Roll into a cone shape, overlapping slightly. Glue or staple where needed (Figure 1).

2. Reproduce, color, and cut out the patterns on page 54. Glue to the cone.

3. Punch a hole on both sides of the cone as shown (Figure 2). To make a hanger for the bird feeder, string a 24" length of ribbon through the holes and tie (Figure 2).

4. Fill the feeder with bird seed. Hang it in a tree where you can watch the birds eat (Figure 3).

Figure 1   Figure 2   Figure 3

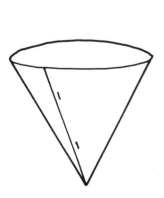

SS2871

Happy Holiday Bells

"On that day HOLY TO THE LORD will be inscribed on the bells of the horses. . . ."

Zechariah 14:20

Materials:
   One 9" paper plate
   Paints, crayons, colored pencils, or
      markers
   Scissors
   Hole punch
   Two jingle bells
   Glue

Related Scripture:
   Psalm 100:1 (KJV)
   Philippians 4:4

   Tape
   Yarn
   Ribbon
   Stapler (optional)

Directions:

1. Color the paper plate and cut in half. Roll each half into a cone shape. Overlapping slightly, glue or staple where needed (Figure 1).

2. Clip off the tips of the cones. Punch a hole near the tip of each cone and thread ribbon through as shown (Figure 2). Tie a pretty bow on top.

3. Tie one end of a 3" piece of yarn to a jingle bell. Attach the other end of the yarn to the inside of the bell with tape. Repeat with the other bell (Figure 3).

4. Reproduce, color, and cut out "Happy Holidays" on page 54, and glue to the bells. Decorate bells with glitter if desired.

Figure 1   Figure 2   Figure 3

Patterns

Christmas Caroler Plate

"In front are the singers, after them the musicians;"   Psalm 68:25a

Materials:
    One 9" paper plate
    Paints, crayons, colored pencils, or
       markers
    Two or three jingle bells
    Yarn
    Scissors
    Hole punch
    Glue

Related Scripture:
    2 Chronicles 5:13
    Psalm 100:2

Directions:
1. Color the front and back of the paper plate.
2. Reproduce, color, and cut out carolers and notes on page 56. Glue to the paper plate front (Figure 1).
3. Punch holes in the plate rim, threading yarn through to tie jingle bells to the plate (Figure 2).
4. Glue music, poems, etc. in the blank plate center (Figure 3). This is great for taking caroling.

Figure 1   Figure 2   Figure 3

          SS2871

Patterns

SS2871

Stained Glass Church Window

"But the fruit of the Spirit is love, joy, peace, patience, kindness, goodness, faithfulness, gentleness and self-control. . . ."   Galatians 5:22-23

Materials:
   Two 9" paper plates
   Paints, crayons, colored pencils, or
      markers
   Construction paper (various colors)
   Scissors
   Glue

Related Scriptures
   Luke 2:14
   Romans 15:33

Directions:
1. Tear small pieces of construction paper. Overlapping the pieces, glue them to the front of one paper plate. Make sure that the surface is covered. With a fine-tip black marker, outline the different pieces of colored paper (Figure 1).
2. Reproduce and cut out the window pattern on page 58. Trace it on the second paper plate front, and cut out the window area as shown (Figure 2).
3. Place the window plate on top of the construction paper plate, and glue the edges together.
4. Reproduce, color, and cut out the lettering and children on page 58. Glue to the plate as shown (Figure 3).

Figure 1	Figure 2	Figure 3

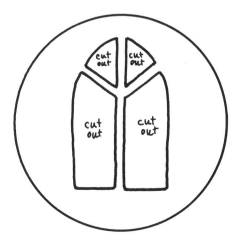
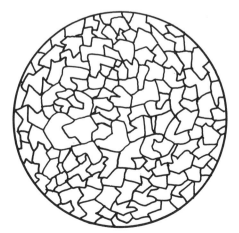

Patterns

Cut out.

SS2871

"Christ Is Born" Mobile

"Today in the town of David a Savior has been born to you; he is Christ the Lord."
                                                                    Luke 2:11

Materials:
  One 9" paper plate
  Paints, crayons, colored pencils, or
    markers
  Yellow construction paper
  Yarn
  Glitter
  Scissors
  Hole punch
  Glue

Related Scripture:
  Matthew 2:1-2
  Luke 2:7

Directions:
1. Color the front of the paper plate blue.
2. Reproduce and cut out the star patterns on pages 60 and 61. Trace stars on yellow construction paper, and cut out.
3. For a three-dimensional look, fold down the top star on the lines as shown on the pattern (Figure 1).
4. Glue the large star to the back of the dimensional star. Then glue these to the paper plate front (Figure 2).
5. Reproduce, color, and cut out the lettering and the manger scene. Punch holes where directed. To complete the mobile, punch holes in the lettering, little stars, and manger scene. Use yarn to attach the mobile pieces to the paper plate. Add glitter to the stars (Figure 3).

Figure 1

Figure 2

Figure 3

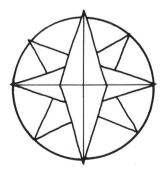

SS2871

Patterns

Fold. Fold.

CHRIST IS BORN!

SS2871

Patterns

SS2871

Cheery Poinsettia Wreath

"A happy heart makes the face cheerful, . . ."   Proverbs 15:13

Materials:
   One 9" paper plate
   Paints, crayons, colored pencils, or
      markers
   Green construction paper
   Tissue paper or waxed paper
   Yarn
   Scissors
   Hole punch
   Glue

Related Scripture:
   Proverbs 15:15
   Proverbs 17:22

Directions:
1. Draw a circle with a 6" diameter in the center of the paper plate. Cut it out, and color the front of the plate (Figure 1).
2. Reproduce, color, and cut out the poinsettia pattern on page 63.
3. Reproduce and cut out the leaf patterns on page 64. Trace and cut out using green construction paper. Glue to the poinsettia (Figure 2).
4. Reproduce and cut out the letters. Trace them on construction paper and cut out. Glue the poinsettia and lettering to the plate rim.
5. To make a hanger, punch a hole in the plate rim, string yarn through the hole, and tie.
6. Cut an 8" circle from tissue paper or waxed paper, and glue to the back of the plate (Figure 3). Let the sun shine through!

Figure 1   Figure 2   Figure 3

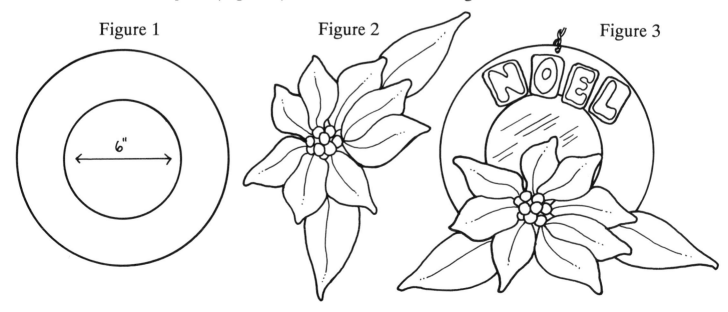

                    SS2871

Pattern

SS2871

Patterns

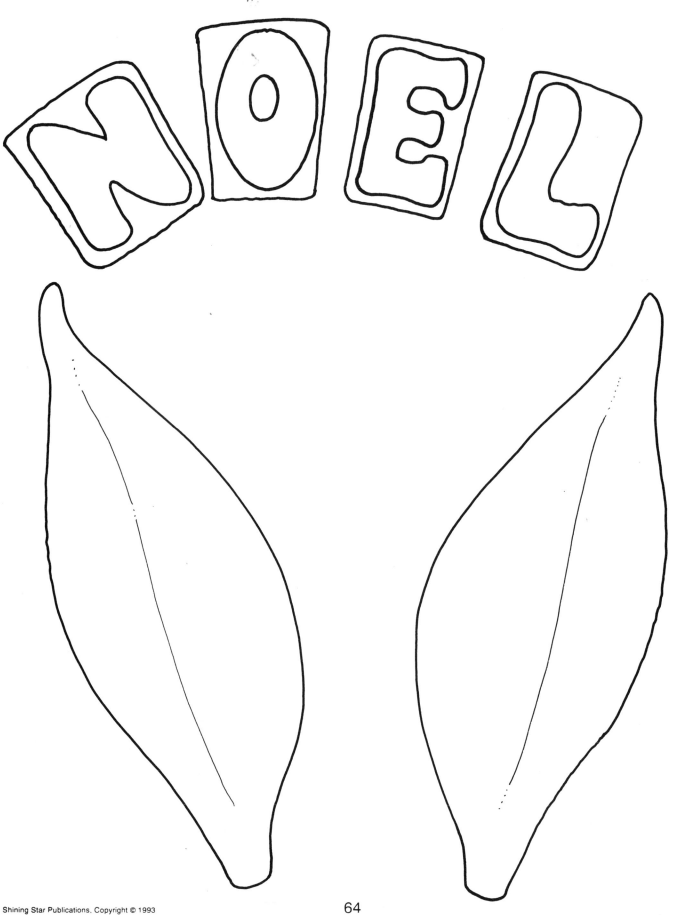

SS2871